DAILY MATH ADVENTURES

by Marcy Cook

Cuisenaire Company of America, Inc.
10 Bank Street. P.O. Box 5026
White Plains, NY 10602-5026

Cover and Illustrations by Rita Formaro

ISBN 0-914040-51-0
Permission is granted for limited reproduction of pages
from this book for classroom use.

Printed in U.S.A.

4 5 6 7 8 9 10 -BK- 02 01 00 99 98

INTRODUCTION

Why use *Daily Math Adventures?*

Students need to practice daily the basic skills of estimation, computation, and problem solving in order to cope with problems in the real world when they no longer have the luxury of a teacher's guidance. This problem-solving ability will help them to become confident and capable adults. Here is a collection of "real world" verbal problems that encourage problem solving as well as computational practice, both with and without a calculator. Unlike the textbook, these problems are purposely not organized around one particular operation.

Who is to use *Daily Math Adventures?*

The problems are appropriate for students in grades 3-8. They cover a wide range of topics, and although there is a theme throughout, the problems are not put in sequence according to the level of difficulty. Some of the exercises are appropriate for extension work for the early grades. Others are useful for remedial work for the upper grades.

How is *Daily Math Adventures* organized?

This book is designed for a school calendar of 180 days. There is a problem for each day of the week plus an additional weekly problem requiring the collection and graphing of data. Each day of the week has a different theme.

Monday problems focus on using a menu. Menus obtained from local restaurants are more meaningful than "pretend" dittoed ones. If children already have the necessary skills, they should be encouraged to figure the tax and tip.

Tuesday problems focus on the immenseness of one million. These problems help students gain better insight into the meaning of large numbers. In this context estimation is important and meaningful, and calculators are helpful.

Wednesday problems focus on the calendar, stressing deductive reasoning: If this, then what? A reproducible blank calendar is provided. It would be helpful if a calendar showing holidays were available to the students.

Thursday problems focus on facts about the human body, the kind found in the *Guiness Book of World Records* and *The Big Book of Amazing Facts*. Here again, the calculator is an extremely useful tool and estimation is helpful.

Friday problems focus on using the newspaper. A supply of recent issues of several local newspapers is necessary. Ask students to keep the supply up-to-date. A variety will make comparative studies possible.

Weekly problems require more time and are appropriate for homework assignments. They usually involve the collecting, sorting, and graphing of data.

How can the classroom teacher use *Daily Math Adventures?*

One suggestion is to give a word problem each day. This can be done in a variety of ways. A problem can be written on the chalkboard, displayed on an overhead projector, posted on the bulletin board, or duplicated and distributed to each student. Another idea is to distribute all of the problems for the next week on Friday. A short discussion should follow the assignment of each problem to be sure that it is understood.

A good first step in the solution process is to ask the students for their estimates. (Students could consider the problems individually, with a partner, or in small groups.) A discussion should follow on possible results and why they might be possible.

When discussing the solutions to the problems, students should be encouraged to tell how he or she reached that conclusion. Many different avenues of thought are possible and no one avenue is more correct than another. Several discussion questions are suggested below.

How can you attack this problem?
What can you conclude? Why?
How can you decide that?
Will the result always be the same?
What assumptions, if any, can you make?
Why does that make sense to you?
How can your calculator help you solve that?

Monday

Use a menu. Order a meal which comes as close as you can to $5.00. Total your bill.

Tuesday

How many dollars do you have if your piggy bank contains a million pennies?

Wednesday

If September 1st is on a Monday, what is the sum of the Monday dates in September?

Thursday

If you breathe a dozen breaths a minute and inhale about a pint of air with each breath, how much air will you breathe in an hour?

Friday

Use a newspaper. Find 10 items, each less than $1.00. What is the total cost?

Daily Math Adventure ©1987 Cuisenaire Co. of America, Inc.

Weekly

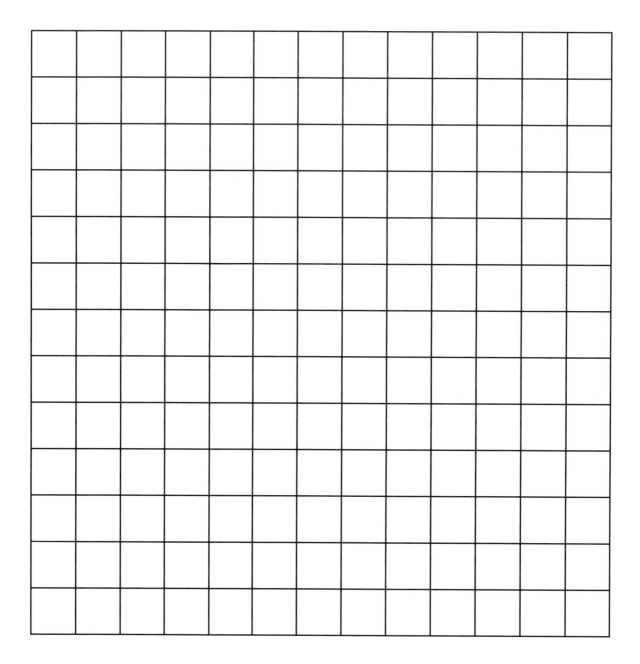

GUESS how many brothers and sisters most people have.

ASK at least 20 unrelated people, "How many brothers and sisters do you have altogether?"

GRAPH each response.

COMPARE your results with others.

WHAT DO YOU CONCLUDE?

Monday

Use a menu. You only have two dollars to spend and you are very hungry! What will you buy? Total the bill.

Tuesday

If you save $1,000 each month, how many years will it take you to become a millionaire?

Wednesday

If September 3rd is on a Saturday, what is the sum of all the Sunday dates in September?

Thursday

If you always eat 3 meals a day, how many meals will you have eaten if you live to be 100?

Friday

Use a newspaper. Look at the front page only. How many articles are on the front page? How many contain at least one number? What fractional amount of the articles contain one or more numbers?

Weekly

If you flip a coin 25 times, will heads or tails come up more often?

Guess how many times each will come up.

HEADS	TAILS	TOTAL

Now flip a coin 25 times. Tally each result.

	HEADS	TAILS	TOTAL
TOTAL			

How does your guess compare with your results?

Compare your results with others.
WHAT DO YOU CONCLUDE?

Use a menu. You have $12.00 but you need to save $3.00 for school supplies. Order a sandwich, a beverage, and dessert. Total the bill.

Tuesday

How many centuries are in a million years?

Wednesday

What is the sum of all the dates in September?

Thursday

If an infant has 300 bones in his or her body and an adult has only 206, how many bones have fused or grown together?

Friday

Use a newspaper. In the real estate section, find the price of the *most* expensive house listed for sale. Find the price of the *least* expensive house listed. What is the difference in price?

Daily Math Adventure ©1987 Cuisenaire Co. of America, Inc.

Weekly

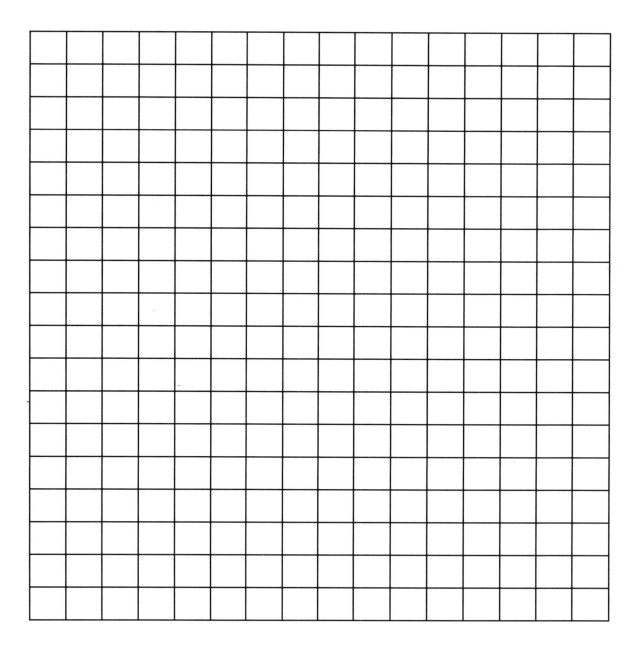

GUESS how many letters most people have in their last name.

MAKE A LIST of the names of at least 20 unrelated people you know.

GRAPH the number of letters in each name. (Example: Cook = 4).

COMPARE your results with others.

WHAT DO YOU CONCLUDE?

Monday

Use a menu. Order something less than 50¢, something between 50¢ and $1.50, and something more than $1.50. Total your bill.

Tuesday

How old will you be if you live a million weeks?

Wednesday

If October 1st is on a Wednesday, what day is Halloween?

Thursday

If your heart beats 120 times a minute, how many times does it beat each day?

Friday

Use a newspaper. Find ads for four items for sale that you would like to buy. *Estimate* the total cost for all four items. *Calculate* the total cost for all four items. Is your estimate more or less than the calculated cost?

Weekly

If you roll a die 25 times, what number will be rolled most often, if any?

Guess how many times each number will be rolled.

1	2	3	4	5	6	TOTAL

Now roll a die 25 times. Tally each result.

	1	2	3	4	5	6	TOTAL
TOTAL							

How did your guess compare with your results?

Compare your results with others.

WHAT DO YOU CONCLUDE?

Monday

Use a menu.
Order breakfast, lunch, and dinner.
Total your bill.

Tuesday

How many classes, all about the size of your class,
does it take to have a million students?

Wednesday

Use a calendar. Pick any 3 numbers in a row. Find
the sum. Do this for another set of 3 in a row. Do
you see a pattern? (Hint: Look at the sum and the
middle number).

Thursday

If during one night's sleep you have from three to
five dreams, approximately how many dreams will
you have in a year?

Friday

Use a newspaper. Choose a page from the classified ad section. How many ads are on the page?
What is the average number of lines per ad?

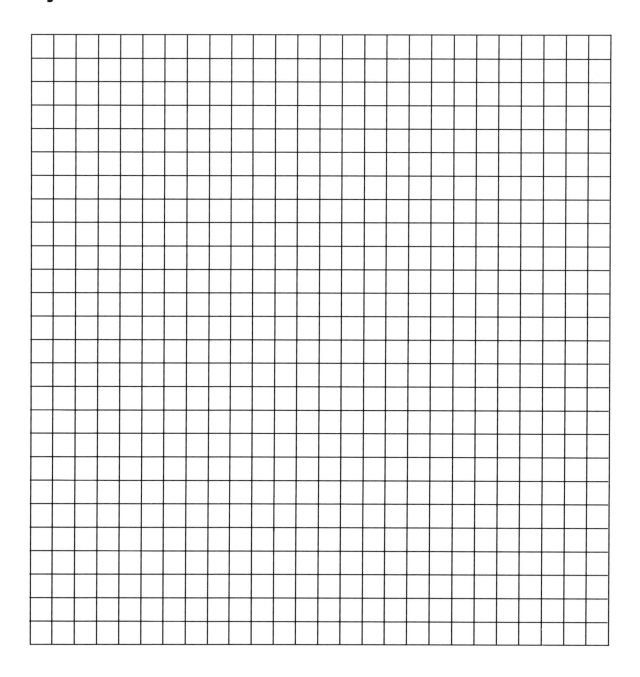

GUESS what letter most frequently begins the spelling of people's first names.

MAKE A LIST of at least 20 different first names of people you know.

GRAPH the beginning letter of each name.

COMPARE your results with others.

WHAT DO YOU CONCLUDE?

Monday

Use a menu.
Order dinner for your entire family.
Total the bill.

Tuesday

How old would you be if you lived a million days?

Wednesday

If election day falls on November 2nd, what is the sum of the dates of Veteran's Day and Thanksgiving Day?

Thursday

If you live to the age of 90, approximately how many days will you have lived?

Friday

Use two different newspapers. Find a travel advertisement to the same place in both newspapers. Compare costs.

Weekly

Numerals are used in many places besides math problems.

Look around you. List at least 20 numerals you find in your school, your home, and outside. Tell how each numeral is used.

SCHOOL	HOME	OUTSIDE

What numeral is used the most?

Monday

Use a menu. There are twelve guests at your party. Order a dessert and a beverage for each person including yourself. Total the bill.

Tuesday

If you have a million dollars and give a hundred dollars away each day, in how many years will you be "broke"?

Wednesday

If November 4th is on a Thursday, what is the date of Thanksgiving?

Thursday

If the normal range of weight is 110-210 pounds for men and 90-175 for women, how far are you from "normal" adult weight?

Friday

Use a newspaper. In the television section, find the names of TV programs that contain a number. (Example: Beverly Hills 90210).

Weekly

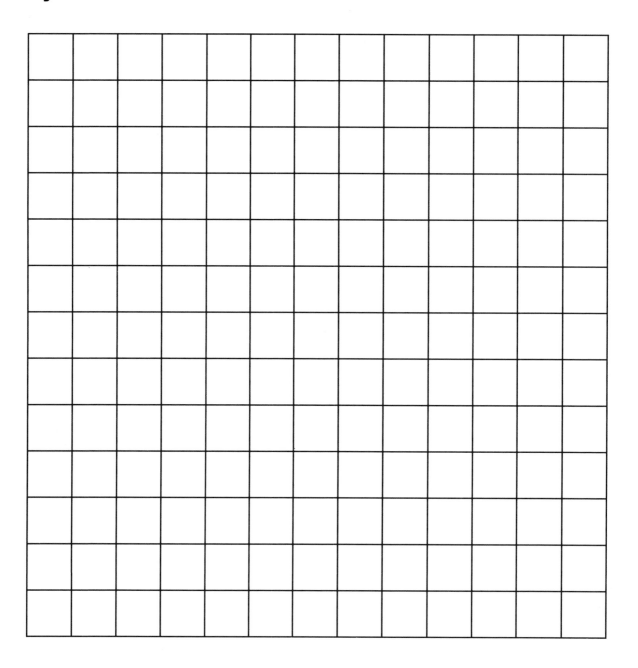

GUESS the number of pets owned by most people.

ASK at least 20 unrelated people, "How many pets do you own?"

GRAPH each response.

COMPARE your results with others.

WHAT DO YOU CONCLUDE?

Monday

Use a menu. Money is no object. You have plenty and are very hungry. Order what you want but be realistic about how much you can eat. Total the bill.

Tuesday

The average number of hairs on a human head is 120,000. How many people does it take to have a million hairs?

Wednesday

If November 22nd is on a Tuesday, what is the sum of the dates of the Saturdays in November?

Thursday

If muscles make up about 40% of your body weight, how much do your muscles weigh?

Friday

Use a newspaper. Look for coupons. How much could you save if you used every coupon in the paper you picked?

Weekly

Place two red checkers and two black checkers in a bag. If you draw a checker from the bag and then return it 25 times, will you get a red checker or a black checker more often?

Guess how many times each will occur.

RED	BLACK	TOTAL

Now place two red checkers and two black checkers in a bag. Draw out a checker and tally the result. Return the checker to the bag. Repeat until you have drawn 25 times.

	RED	BLACK	TOTAL
TOTAL			

How does your guess compare with your results?

Compare your results with others.

WHAT DO YOU CONCLUDE?

Use a menu. Order five different items on the menu.
Total the bill.

Tuesday

If your heart beats 72 times a minute, how many
days does it take your heart to beat a million times?

Wednesday

If December 1st is on a Saturday, what is the sum
of all the weekend dates (Saturdays and Sundays)
in December?

Thursday

If you blink your eyes about 25 times a minute, how
many times will you blink in a twelve-hour period
of time?

Friday

Use a newspaper. In ads, find four items that are
sold by the pound. Find the cost of five pounds of
each item. Total the cost.

Weekly

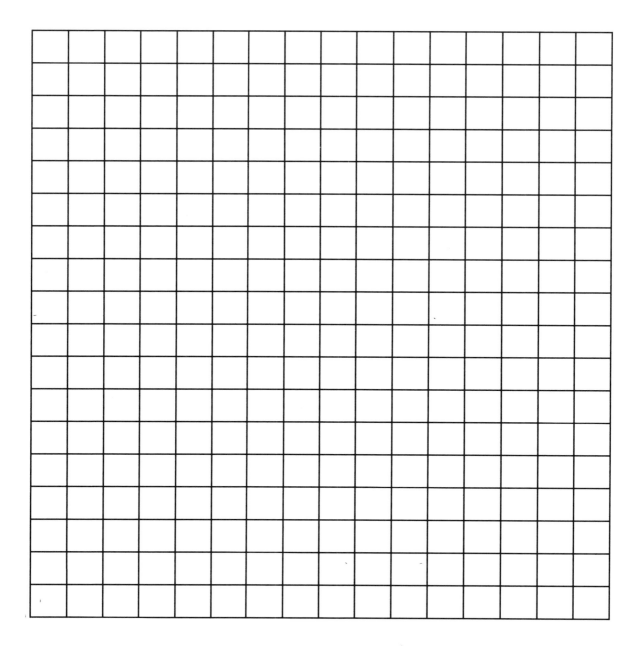

GUESS how many seconds you can stand on one foot, with your eyes closed.

WORK with a partner. Have your partner time each attempt. Do this 10 times.

GRAPH your times.

COMPARE your results with others.

WHAT DO YOU CONCLUDE?

Use a menu. Order the best meal and beverage for your friend who is trying to lose weight. Total the bill.

Tuesday

If you sleep 10 hours a day for 365 days a year, how old would you be after sleeping a million hours?

Wednesday

If December 7th is on a Thursday, on what day of the week does Christmas fall? On what day does New Year's Eve fall?

Thursday

If blood travels round trip from the heart, through the body, and back to the heart again in less than a minute, about how many round trips are made in a day?

Friday

Use a newspaper. In the grocery advertisements, find five different items whose total cost is $10.00 or as close to it as possible.

Weekly

How many books are in your school library?

Think of a way to estimate this without counting every book or asking the librarian. Use it to estimate the number of books in your school library.

Now ask your librarian how many books are in the library.

How close was your estimate to the actual number?

Compare your way of estimating with others.
WHAT DO YOU CONCLUDE?

Daily Math Adventure ©1987 Cuisenaire Co. of America, Inc.

Monday

Use a menu. Order soup, salad, a sandwich *or* main dish, a beverage, *and* a dessert. Total the bill.

Tuesday

If you have a million dollars and give a thousand dollars away each day, in how many days will you be "broke"?

Wednesday

If New Year's Eve is on a Thursday, what is the sum of the dates of the Mondays in December?

Thursday

If there are 800 red cells for every one white cell, how many white cells would be in a drop of blood which contains 250 million red cells?

Friday

Use a newspaper. Find three examples that use numbers larger than 1,000. Explain each.

Weekly

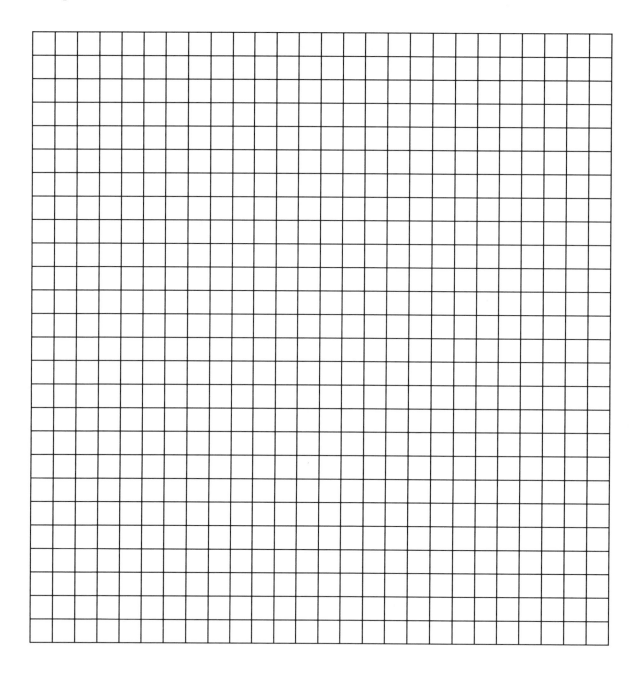

GUESS what letter most frequently begins the spelling of people's last names.

MAKE A LIST of at least 20 different last names of people you know.

GRAPH the beginning letter of each name.

COMPARE your graph with others.

WHAT DO YOU CONCLUDE?

Monday

Use a menu. Find the best buy for your money when ordering a complete meal and beverage. Total the bill.

Tuesday

A child's heart may beat 120 times a minute. In how many days will it beat a million times?

Wednesday

If Christmas is on Thursday, what is the sum of the dates of the Mondays in January?

Thursday

Since you lose water as you breathe and sweat, you need to have about 2½ quarts of water a day to stay healthy. How much water do you need in a year?

Friday

Use a newspaper. Find 5 common fractions and explain how each is used.

Weekly

Two straight lines are said to be perpendicular to each other if they intersect or meet at right angles. The angles formed each measure 90°.

Look around you. List at least 10 examples of perpendicular lines you find in your school, your home, and outside.

SCHOOL	HOME	OUTSIDE

Where did you find the most examples of perpendicular lines?

Monday

Use a menu. Order lunch for three people so that each food or beverage is only ordered once. Total the bill.

Tuesday

How old would you be if you lived a million minutes?

Wednesday

If the exact middle day of January is a Tuesday, what day is January 31st?

Thursday

If your body uses 2,000 calories per day, how many will it use in a lifetime of 70 years?

Friday

Use a newspaper. Read the comics. What numbers or math references do you find?

Daily Math Adventure ©1987 Cuisenaire Co. of America, Inc.

Weekly

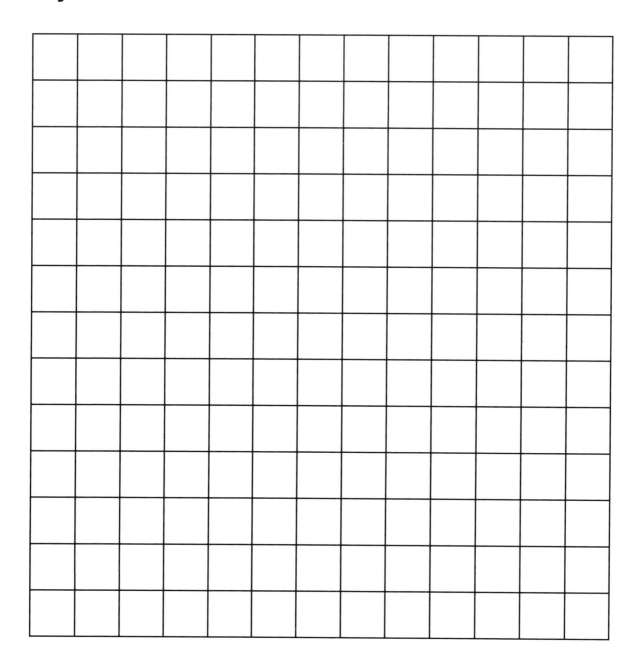

GUESS what sum would most likely occur if you rolled a pair of dice and added the result.

ROLL a pair of dice. Add the numbers. Do this at least 20 times.

GRAPH each sum.

COMPARE your results with others.

WHAT DO YOU CONCLUDE?

Monday

Use a menu. Order a meal that contains food from each of the four basic food groups: milk products, meat, grains, and fruits/vegetables. Total the bill.

Tuesday

If an elephant's heart beats 25 times a minute, how many days does it take to beat a million times?

Wednesday

If the 1st of the month is on a Monday, what is the sum of the dates of the four full work weeks (Monday through Friday) for that month?

Thursday

If you make an average of three phone calls a day, how many will you make a year?

Friday

Use a newspaper. Look in the Lost And Found section. What is the highest reward being offered? How much? Why?

Weekly

Do the same number of cars pass your house or school each day at the same time?

Choose a five-minute period of time. (Example: 2:50 P.M. to 2:55 P.M.). Guess how many cars will pass by during that five-minute period of time.

For five days in a row, tally the number of cars that pass during your five-minute period. Use a stopwatch or wristwatch.

DAY 1	DAY 2	DAY 3	DAY 4	DAY 5

Did the same number pass each day?

If not, which day was closest to your guess?

Compare your results with others.

WHAT DO YOU CONCLUDE?

Use two different menus. Order the two most expensive items from each menu. Total each bill. What is the difference?

If you make a million marks with your pencil and it takes one second for each mark, how long will it take you to complete the marks?

If Valentine's Day is on a Tuesday, what is the sum of the dates of all two-digit Mondays in February?

If you take about 1,000 breaths every hour, how many breaths will you take a year?

Use a newspaper. How many pictures with captions are located in the front section? How many words are usually used in a caption?

Weekly

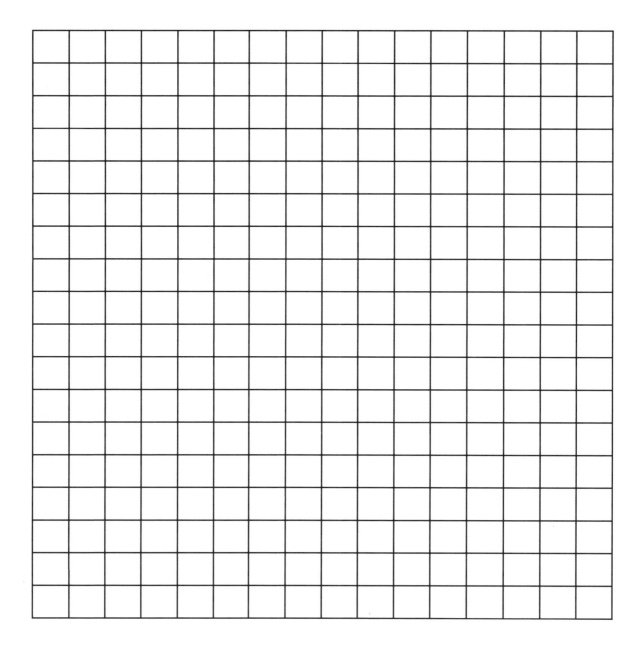

GUESS which number between 1 and 10 is the favorite of most people.

ASK at least 20 different people, "What is your favorite number from 1 through 10?"

GRAPH each response.

COMPARE your results with others.

WHAT DO YOU CONCLUDE?

Monday

Use a menu. You are in charge of arrangements for a luncheon. Order the same lunch for 25 people. Find the cost.

Tuesday

If you live to be 70 years of age, you will be a minute multimillionaire. How many minutes will you have lived?

Wednesday

If the sum of the dates of the first weekend in February is 11, what are the sums of the dates of each of the other weekends that month?

Thursday

The words you are reading now are being sent to your brain by 1¼ million receptors located in your eyes. When eight people are reading at the same time, how many receptors are sending signals?

Friday

Use a newspaper. Find a food item you can buy for each member of your class. Figure the cost.

Weekly

If you draw one card from a regular deck of 52 playing cards and then return it 25 times, what suit will you draw most often?

Guess how many times each will come up.

HEARTS	DIAMONDS	CLUBS	SPADES	TOTAL

Now draw a card from a regular deck of 52 playing cards and tally the result. Return the card to the deck. Mix the deck. Repeat until you have drawn 25 times.

	HEARTS	DIAMONDS	CLUBS	SPADES	TOTAL
TOTAL					

How does your guess compare your results?

Compare your results with others.
WHAT DO YOU CONCLUDE?

Monday

Use a menu. Order four of the same item for your friend and yourself. Total the bill.

Tuesday

If you earn $20,000 a year, in how many years will you earn a million dollars?

Wednesday

If a leap year has a Friday the 13th in February, on what day of the week is the first of March?

Thursday

If there are 250 million red blood cells in a drop of blood, how many red cells would you lose if your knee dripped 10 drops of blood?

Friday

Use a newspaper. In the classified ad section, find the *most* expensive used car offered. Find the *least* expensive used car offered. What is the difference in price?

Weekly

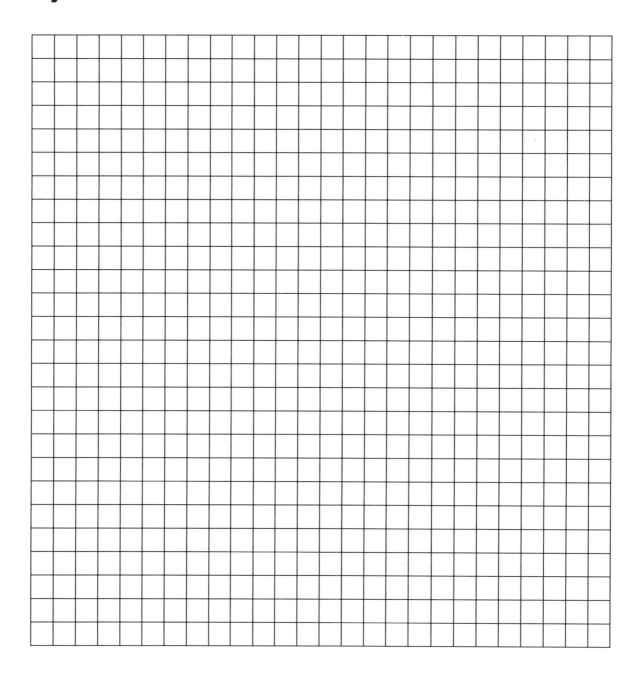

GUESS which letter is most often used in spelling the months of the year.

MAKE A LIST of the months of the year.

GRAPH the number of times each letter is used.

COMPARE your results with others.

WHAT DO YOU CONCLUDE?

Use a menu. Order one of every beverage. Total the bill. Find the average cost of a beverage on this menu.

How many dozen eggs must you buy to have one million eggs?

The sum of the dates of the first full work week (Monday through Friday) of a month is exactly half the sum of the dates of the second full work week. What day is the 1st of that month?

The average person in the United States eats 11 ounces of meat each day. How many pounds of meat will that person eat in a year?

Use a newspaper. Find the highest and lowest recorded temperatures in the nation. Where did they occur? What is the difference between the two?

Weekly

Geometric shapes of triangles, circles, and squares are found in many places besides math lessons.

Look around you. List at least 3 examples of each shape you find in your school, your home, and outside.

	SCHOOL	HOME	OUTSIDE
TRIANGLE			
SQUARE			
CIRCLE			

Which shape appears most often?

Use a menu. You have a five-dollar bill. You take a friend to lunch. Your friend orders first. His lunch is almost $3.00. Then you order. What do you order? What does your friend order? Total your bill.

How many $25,000-cars can you purchase with one million dollars?

If the dates in March that are multiples of ten fall on Sunday, Wednesday, and Saturday, what day of the week is March 1st? What day of the week is March 25th?

If your skin weighs twice as much as your brain, and your brain weighs twice as much as a 1½ pound rock, how much does your skin weigh?

Use a newspaper. Choose five advertisements of different sizes. *Estimate* the area of each ad. *Find* the area of each ad. Compare.

Weekly

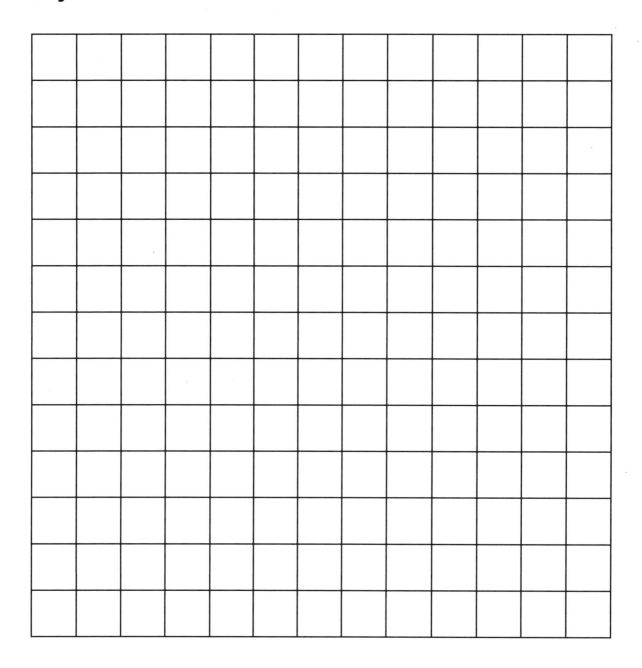

GUESS which is the favorite color of most people.

ASK at least 20 people, "What is your favorite color?"

GRAPH each response.

COMPARE your results to others.

WHAT DO YOU CONCLUDE?

Use a menu. Order two different meals, including a beverage, whose totals are as close to the same amount as possible. Total each bill.

Tuesday

Does the city or town where you live have more or less than a million people? How many more or less?

Wednesday

If March 16th is on a Sunday, what days in March will have the dates that are multiples of 5? What day will not be a multiple of 5?

Thursday

More than 20 elements make up the human body. Hydrogen (63%) and oxygen (25.5%) are the most common. What percent of the human body do the rest of the elements represent?

Friday

Use a newspaper. Choose five advertisements, which differ in size. *Estimate* the perimeter of each ad. *Find* the perimeter of each ad. Compare.

Weekly

Choose a book. How many words are in it?

Make a guess and record.

Now approximate the number of words in the book, using a method of your choice.
Record your approximation.

Compare your guess and your approximation.

Choose a second book. How many words are in it?

Make a guess and record.

Now approximate the number of words in the book, using a method of your choice.
Record your approximation.

Compare your guess and your approximation.

For which book was your guess closest to your approximation?

Monday

Use a menu. Order one of every dessert. Total the bill. Find the average cost of dessert on this menu.

Tuesday

How old will you be if you live a million months?

Wednesday

If the sum of two consecutive Wednesdays in March is 45, what day of the week is March 1st? What day of the week is the last day in March?

Thursday

If you can donate five pints of blood each year, how much could you donate over a forty-year period of time?

Friday

Use a newspaper. How many different sizes of type can you find? How many letters of the largest type are there in one centimeter? How many letters of the smallest type are there in one centimeter?

Weekly

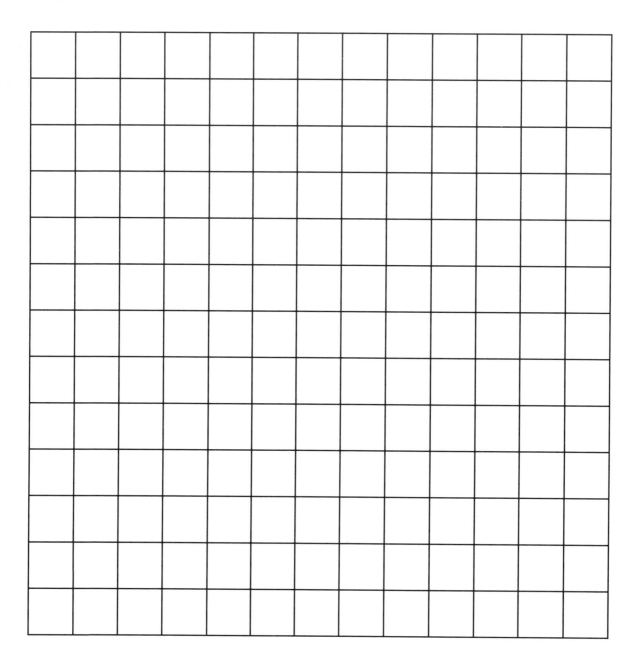

GUESS which television program is most popular.

ASK at least 20 people, "What is your favorite show on TV?"

GRAPH each response.

COMPARE your results with others.

WHAT DO YOU CONCLUDE?

Monday

Use a menu. Find three items you could eat for lunch that adults would consider nutritious. Total the bill.

Tuesday

If the fastest talker can speak 300 words per minute, how long will it take him or her to speak a million words?

Wednesday

If Easter is on April 11th, what is the sum of the dates of all Sundays between Easter and the 4th of July?

Thursday

If the earliest human relic is a skull from 22,000 B.C., how old is it?

Friday

Use a newspaper. Find grocery ads for 2 different grocery stores. List the items that both stores are advertising. Record the cost of each item and compare.

Daily Math Adventure ©1987 Cuisenaire Co. of America, Inc.

Weekly

Place three red checkers and one black checker in a bag. If you draw a checker from the bag and then return it 25 times, will you get a red checker or a black check more often?

Guess how many times each will occur.

RED	BLACK	TOTAL

Now place three red checkers and one black checker in a bag. Draw out a checker and tally the result. Return the checker to the bag. Repeat until you have drawn 25 times.

	RED	BLACK	TOTAL
TOTAL			

How does your guess compare with your results?

Compare your results with others.

WHAT DO YOU CONCLUDE?

Monday

Use a menu. Order all your meals including snacks for two days. Total the bill.

Tuesday

How old would you be if you lived a million hours?

Wednesday

If the sum of the dates of the first Sunday, Monday, Tuesday, and Wednesday in April is 30, what day of the week is April Fool's Day? What day of the week is April 30th?

Thursday

If you drink a 12-ounce can of soda each day, how many gallons will you drink in a year?

Friday

Use a newspaper. Find a report on the tides. What is the difference between the highest high-tide and lowest low-tide?

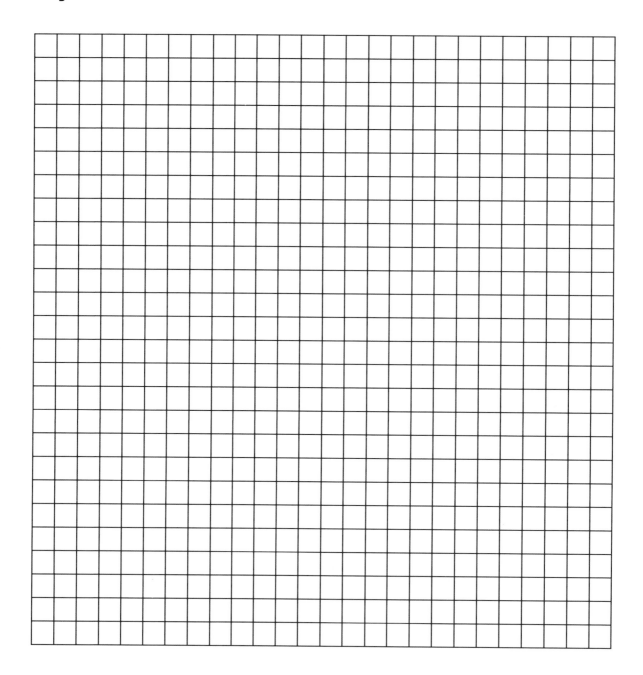

GUESS which letter most frequently begins the last names of presidents of the United States.

MAKE A LIST of all the presidents of the United States.

GRAPH the initial letter of each last name.

COMPARE your results with others.

WHAT DO YOU CONCLUDE?

Use two different menus. Order the same three items from both menus. Total each bill. What is the difference?

Tuesday

If a mouse's heart beats 700 times a minute, how long will it take to beat a million times?

Wednesday

What is the largest possible sum for all Monday dates in any month?

Thursday

If the hair on your head grows about half an inch each month, how long would it take your hair to grow one foot (assuming it does not break)?

Friday

Use a newspaper. Find five different percents and explain how each is used.

Weekly

Straight lines are said to be parallel if they are always the same distance apart.

Look around you. List at least 10 examples of parallel lines you find in your school, your home, and outside.

SCHOOL	HOME	OUTSIDE

Where did you find the most examples of parallel lines?

Monday

Use a menu. Order hamburgers, french fries, and chocolate shakes for your best friend and yourself. Total the bill.

Tuesday

How many of your math books would you have to pile on top of each other to have a stack one million centimeters high?

Wednesday

What is the smallest possible sum for all Wednesday dates in any month?

Thursday

Marathon runners may record a body temperature as high as 105.8° Fahrenheit in hot weather. How much higher than normal body temperature is this?

Friday

Use a newspaper. Find the times of the highest and lowest temperatures in the city nearest to you. How many hours passed between the highest temperature and the lowest?

Weekly

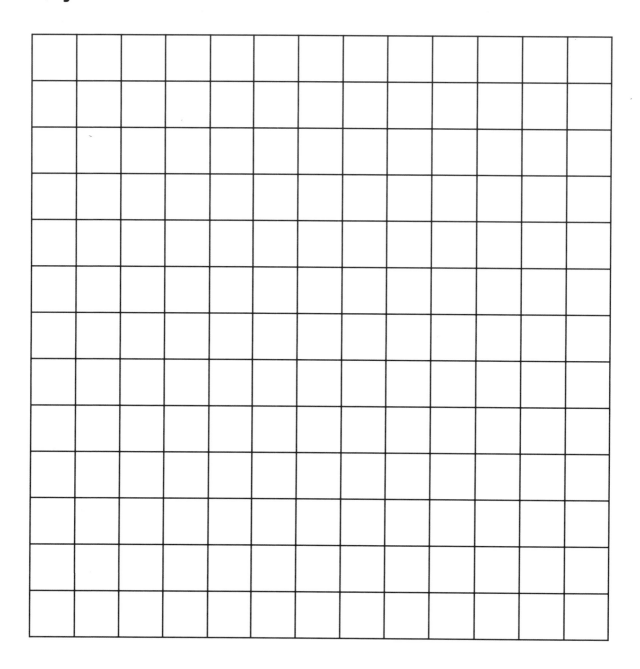

GUESS which month has the most birthdays.

ASK at least 20 people, "In what month were you born?"

GRAPH each response.

COMPARE your results with others.

WHAT DO YOU CONCLUDE?

Monday

Use a menu. You order the *least* expensive sandwich, beverage, and dessert. Your friend orders the *most* expensive sandwich, beverage, and dessert. Total each bill. Find the difference.

Tuesday

How many $200-motorbikes can you purchase with one million dollars?

Wednesday

If the sum of the dates of the last full week (from Sunday through Saturday) of May is 175, what day of the week is May 1st? What day of the week is the last day of May?

Thursday

If about 18% of a 160-pound man's weight is the weight of his bones, what do his bones weigh?

Friday

Use a newspaper. Plan dinner for 4 people. Make a shopping list. Find the total cost.

Daily Math Adventure ©1987 Cuisenaire Co. of America, Inc.

Do you think more books are listed in a library card file under Q, U, V, X, Y or Z?

Make a guess and record.

Use a card file in your school or public library. Count the entries for each of these six letters. Record your count.

Q	U	V	X	Y	Z

Which letter has the most entries?

Which letter has the least number of entries?

How does your guess compare with your results?

Daily Math Adventure ©1987 Cuisenaire Co. of America, Inc.

Monday

Use a menu. Order one of every sandwich. Total the bill. Find the average cost of a sandwich on this menu.

Tuesday

If 100 people in every million have an I.Q. above 160, how many people in your state have an I.Q. of more than 160?

Wednesday

Use a calendar. Pick any 3 numbers in a column. Find the sum. Do this for another set of 3 in a column. Do you see a pattern? (Hint: Look at the sum the middle number).

Thursday

If you laughed fifteen times each day, how many times would you laugh in a year?

Friday

Use a newspaper. In ads, find five different clothing items whose total cost is $25.00 or as close to it as possible.

Daily Math Adventure ©1987 Cuisenaire Co. of America, Inc.

Weekly

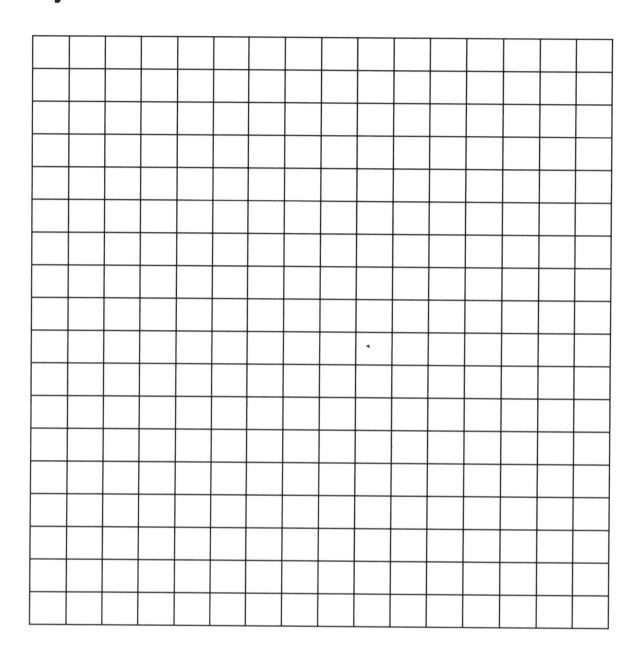

GUESS the average height of adults.

ASK at least 20 adults their height.

GRAPH each height.

COMPARE your results with others.

WHAT DO YOU CONCLUDE?

Monday

Use a menu. Order a meal that would be as close to $25.00 as possible, but not over. Total the bill.

Tuesday

How old would you be if you lived a million seconds?

Wednesday

If the sum of the dates in June preceding Father's Day is 190, what date is Father's Day?

Thursday

If you eat six ounces of sugar every day, how many pounds of sugar do you eat in a year?

Friday

Use a newspaper. Find the current prices for gold, silver, and three other metals.

Weekly

If you draw one card from a regular deck of 52 playing cards and then return it 25 times, what will you draw most often—an ace, a number card, or a face card?

Guess how many times each will come up.

ACE	NUMBER	FACE	TOTAL

Now draw a card from a regular deck of 52 playing cards and tally the result. Return the card to the deck. Mix the deck. Repeat until you have drawn 25 times.

	ACE	NUMBER	FACE	TOTAL
TOTAL				

How does your guess compare with your results?

Compare your results with others.
WHAT DO YOU CONCLUDE?

Answers

Page 5

Mon: varies
Tues: $10,000
Wed: 75
Thurs: 720 pints
Fri: varies

Page 7

Mon: varies
Tues: 83⅓ years
Wed: 58
Thurs: 109,500 meals
Fri: varies

Page 9

Mon: varies
Tues: 10,000 centuries
Wed: 465
Thurs: 94 bones
Fri: varies

Page 11

Mon: varies
Tues: about 19,230 years old
Wed: Friday
Thurs: 172,800 times
Fri: varies

Page 13

Mon: varies
Tues: varies (if 20 students, then 50,000 classes)
Wed: sum=3 times the middle number
Thurs: from 1,095 to 1,825 dreams
Fri: varies

Page 15

Mon: varies
Tues: almost 2,740 years old
Wed: 36
Thurs: about 32,850 days
Fri: varies

Page 17

Mon: varies
Tues: almost 28 years
Wed: November 25th
Thurs: varies
Fri: varies

Page 19

Mon: varies
Tues: at least 9 people
Wed: 62
Thurs: varies
Fri: varies

Page 21

Mon: varies
Tues: almost 10 days
Wed: 155
Thurs: 18,000 times
Fri: varies

Page 23

Mon: varies
Tues: almost 274 years old
Wed: Monday; Sunday
Thurs: at least 1,440 round trips
Fri: varies

Page 25

Mon: varies
Tues: 1,000 days
Wed: 70
Thurs: 312,500 white cells
Fri: varies

Page 27

Mon: varies
Tues: almost 6 days
Wed: 62
Thurs: 912½ quarts
Fri: varies

Page 29

Mon: varies
Tues: almost 2 years old
Wed: Wednesday
Thurs: 51,100,000 calories
Fri: varies

Page 31

Mon: varies
Tues: almost 28 days
Wed: 270
Thurs: 1,095 phone calls
Fri: varies

Page 33

Mon: varies
Tues: about 11½ days, writing 24 hours a day
Wed: 60
Thurs: 8,760,000 breaths
Fri: varies

Page 35

Mon: varies
Tues: 36,792,000 minutes
Wed: 25; 39; 53
Thurs: 10,000,000 receptors
Fri: varies

Answers

Page 37

Mon: varies
Tues: 50 years
Wed: Monday
Thurs: 2,500,000,000 red cells
Fri: varies

Page 39

Mon: varies
Tues: 83,333⅓ dozen
Wed: Thursday
Thurs: almost 251 pounds
Fri: varies

Page 41

Mon: varies
Tues: 40 cars
Wed: Friday; Monday
Thurs: 6 pounds
Fri: varies

Page 43

Mon: varies
Tues: varies
Wed: All days but Friday; Friday
Thurs: 11.5%
Fri: varies

Page 45

Mon: varies
Tues: 83,333⅓ years old
Wed: Saturday; Monday
Thurs: 200 pints
Fri: varies

Page 47

Mon: varies
Tues: 3,333⅓ minutes for almost 56 hours
Wed: 189
Thurs: 22,000 + current year (if 1987, then 23,987 years old)
Fri: varies

Page 49

Mon: varies
Tues: about 114 years old
Wed: Tuesday; Wednesday
Thurs: over 34 gallons
Fri: varies

Page 51

Mon: varies
Tues: about 1,428 minutes or almost 24 hours
Wed: 85 in a month with 31 days where the 31st is on a Monday
Thurs: 24 months or 2 years
Fri: varies

Page 53

Mon: varies
Tues: varies
Wed: 46 in February of a non-leap year
Thurs: 7.2°
Fri: varies

Page 55

Mon: varies
Tues: 5,000 motorbikes
Wed: Sunday; Tuesday
Thurs: about 29 pounds
Fri: varies

Page 57

Mon: varies
Tues: varies
Wed: sum=3 times the middle number
Thurs: 5,475 times
Fri: varies

Page 59

Mon: varies
Tues: 11½ days old
Wed: June 20
Thurs: almost 137 pounds
Fri: varies

Page 61

Mon: varies
Tues: 200,000 pounds
Wed: 180 days; 185 days
Thurs: at least 84 changes
Fri: varies